Abbie is Stranded

Written by
Catherine Shaw

Illustrated by
Steve Goodwin

Hello everyone, my name is Colin. I live in a small fishing village called Tideswell.

I work as a Coastguard with my dog Rocky. I have to make sure that people are safe when they are at sea, on the cliffs or on the beach.

If anyone is in trouble I can contact my friends who are always ready to help.

Now read how

Abbie is Stranded

It was a bright, breezy morning. Colin the Coastguard and his dog Rocky were on the cliff top, looking out to sea.

Colin had parked his truck close to a picnic area.

Suddenly, out in Tideswell Bay, Colin saw two huge jets of water spurt into the air.

Colin rubbed his eyes
and looked again.

"Did you see that Rocky,
I wonder what it is?"

Rocky barked and
jumped on to Colin's
truck to get a
better view.

Through his binoculars, Colin could see two whales. The smaller whale was called Abbie.

Nearby, a pod of dolphins was leaping in and out of the water.

Slippy the seagull was flying along the coast. He spotted Colin's truck, squawked, and flew down to land on the cliff top.

Rocky saw Slippy and jumped down from Colin's truck. He bounded across the grass to meet his friend.

LITTER

Suddenly, Rocky yelped with pain. He was holding up his paw. Colin ran towards him.

Colin saw that Rocky had cut his paw. He had trodden on some broken glass.

"We must take you to the vet right away," said Colin.

Colin drove back to Tideswell and carried Rocky into Mrs Sharma's surgery.

"Oh Rocky, what have you done?" she asked. "Let me take a look."

"I will wash the cut and bandage your paw. It will soon feel much better."

Meanwhile, the ferryboat from Pebble Island was out in the bay. The passengers on the ferryboat had seen the dolphins and the two whales.

The children were shouting excitedly. They were rushing from side to side to get a better look.

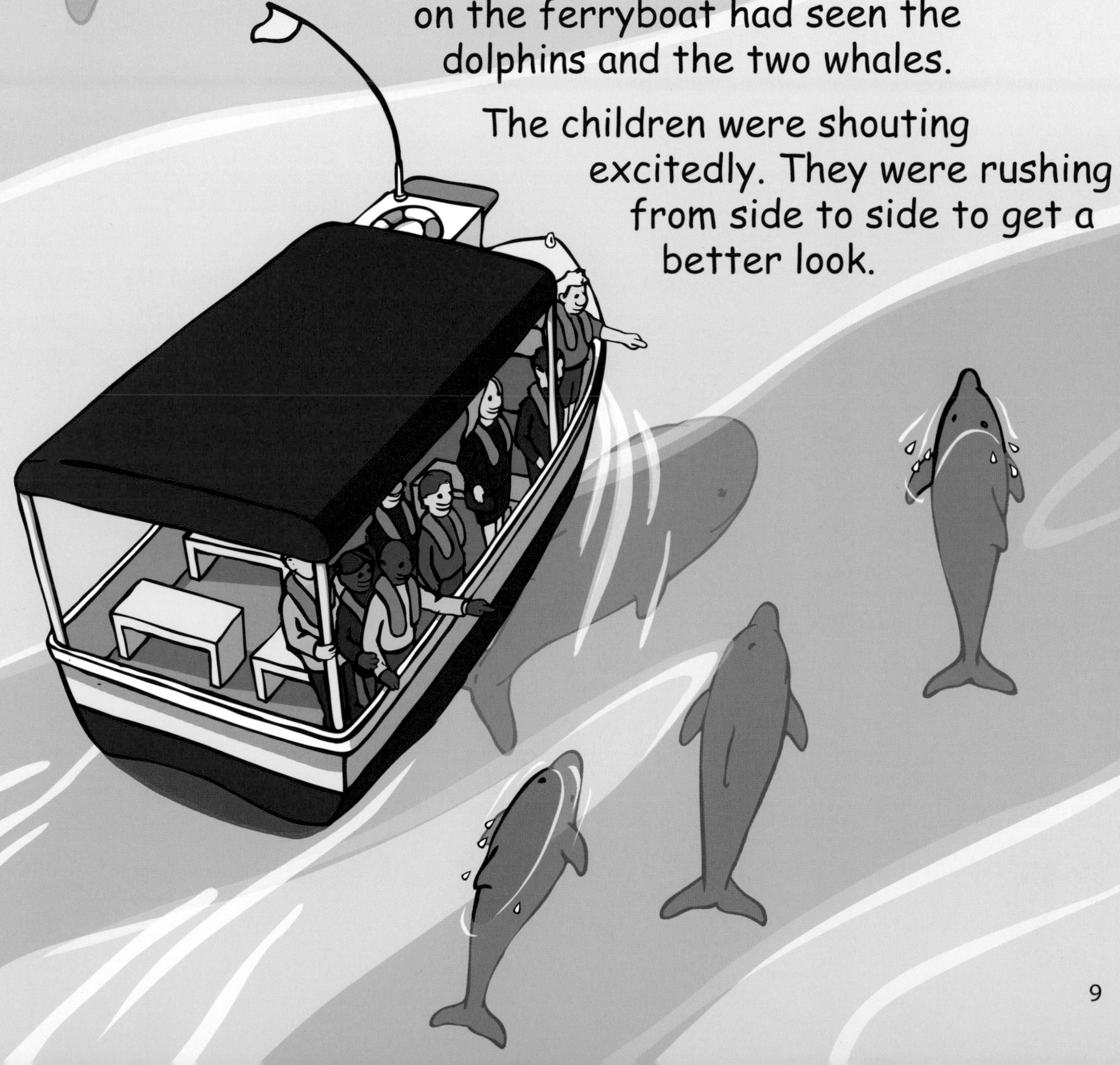

Abbie's mother swam away from the noise, but Abbie stayed with the dolphins. They were having such fun, diving under the ferryboat and coming up on the other side.

Abbie joined in their game and didn't realise her mother had swum away.

Abbie was having a wonderful time!

The children laughed and screamed when Abbie showered them with water. The dolphins swam away, but Abbie followed the ferryboat!

The water became shallower and shallower, and the ferryman saw that Abbie was in trouble.

He phoned Colin, "There's a young whale heading for the beach and she may need help!" he said.

Colin phoned Embers, the Fire Truck Officer, and told him about the whale.

"Down to the beach, quick as you can!" said Colin.

"Right away", said Embers. "I'll see you there."

Then Mrs Sharma offered to help.

"Okay, come with us!" said Colin.

Embers drove his fire truck through the village, with its lights flashing to clear the way. In three minutes he was at the beach!

The little whale was lying at the edge of the sea, flapping her tail and looking very unhappy.

Abbie was stranded!

When Colin and Mrs Sharma arrived, Embers had already parked his fire truck on the beach...

...he was spraying sea-water all over the little whale's body, to keep her cool and wet.

Colin and Mrs Sharma put some floats beside the little whale, to make her more comfortable.

Mrs Sharma stayed close to Abbie, talking quietly, to keep her calm.

"When the tide comes in and the water is deeper, you'll be able to swim again," she whispered.

At last the tide turned and the water came rushing back towards the shore.

Gradually, as the water became deeper, Abbie floated up. Soon, she was ready to swim away to find her mother.

But where was Abbie's mother?

Slippy knew!

Slippy flew overhead, to show Abbie the way. The little whale swam out into the bay, where her mother was waiting for her.

Abbie was so pleased to be safely back with her mother.

At the beach,
Embers had packed
up and was ready
to leave.

"Thank you!"
Colin said to
Embers and Mrs
Sharma. "You both
worked really hard to help
the little whale."

Colin drove Mrs Sharma back to the surgery. He then returned to the picnic area to clear away the litter.

"This glass is sharp!" Colin said to Rocky, "I'd better put on special gloves."

Colin carefully picked up all the litter and placed it in the bin.

When they had finished, Colin and Rocky sat together on the cliff top. Slippy perched on the grass beside them.

The sun was setting and they could see the waterspouts of the two whales out at sea.

"Look Rocky they're together again!" said Colin, "I'm sure Abbie will stay close to her mother from now on!"

THE END

Your Search Mission!

A. How many dolphins can you see on page 5?

B. How did Rocky cut his paw?

C. What did Mrs Sharma put on Rocky's paw?

D. How many people can you see on the ferry on page 11?

E. How long did it take Embers to reach the beach?

F. How did Embers keep Abbie cool?

G. Who can you see in Colin's truck on page 15?

H. Who knew where to find Abbie's mother?

I. Why did Colin and Rocky go back to the picnic area?

J. What colour are Colin's gloves on page 20?

K. How many times can you see Colin's truck in the whole book?

Answers: A = 3 B = Trod on broken glass C = Bandage D = 6 E = Three minutes F = Sprayed her with sea water G = Rocky H = Slippy the Seagull I = To pick up the broken glass and litter J = Red K = 7

Some of Colin's friends who are always ready to help:
Winch - Tugboat Captain
Mrs Sharma - The Vet
Tideswell Veterinary Surgery
Goodwin - Lifeboat Coxswain
Embers - Fire Truck Officer
FIRE
Chesil - Search and Rescue Helicopter Pilot